The Ribbon Bow Shoes

Dr. Beth Christoff

NEWMAN SPRINGS PUBLISHING
320 Broad Street
Red Bank, NJ 07701

First originally published by Newman Springs Publishing 2024

ISBN 979-8-89061-489-6 (Hardcover)
ISBN 979-8-89061-488-9 (Digital)

Printed in the United States of America

To Kathy, Jeanne, and Rita

Did you ever have a moment when your mind drifted to thoughts of your past? Was there something that triggered such a thought, such a memory? Could it be the sweet smell of a flower or the sun warmly shining on your face?

One sunny day, I had such a memory. It was truly an out-of-body experience! I think I was sitting on a chair enjoying the warm summer breeze that was softly caressing my cheeks. I remember the beautiful scent of the nearby lilac bush. Suddenly I was curious and excited about this furry, green caterpillar that appeared at my feet.

He stopped as if to look at me. I rubbed my eyes and blinked to focus better on this little critter. When I was able to get a clear look at him, he was slithering toward a house. I think I started to follow him, being careful not to scare or alarm him. I really wanted to know where he was going and what he was doing.

The caterpillar slid up the stairs and into the house. I waited a bit and then followed him. The door was open, and the surroundings seemed so familiar. I watched as he slid into the kitchen and then into the front room. I heard the voices of young girls laughing. I could see them playing with their dolls. The one little girl had a nurse's cap on her head. She looked just like my younger sister, Kathy. As I came closer, it looked like she was pretending to help her sick doll. I stood there amazed and could feel my eyes well up with tears. I wiped away a tear as it rolled down my cheek.

Kathy and her friend didn't see the little caterpillar, nor did they see me. I was invisible to both of them! The caterpillar moved quickly past the girls and up the stairs. I reluctantly followed him, wishing my sister had noticed me and that we had spoken to each other. As I climbed the stairs, I felt I had been there before and had heard the creaking noise of the steps as I ascended one step at a time.

I followed the furry creature as he meandered up the staircase, passing several bedrooms and a bathroom. He finally decided to enter the last room at the very end of the hallway. It was a small room, and I had seen this room before with the built-in desk, single bed, and chair. To my astonishment, I saw a girl with auburn curls sitting in the chair and reading. The book was covering her face as she intently read. I was positive it was my older sister, Jeanne. Her teachers always said that she was a voracious reader and could never get enough books to satisfy her enormous appetite for reading.

Jeanne didn't notice the caterpillar slide past her, nor did she look up to notice me. I think I tried to speak to her, but I couldn't hear the words come out of my mouth. I wanted very much to talk with her and to hear her voice. At that moment, I was sad and confused, and I looked away to get control of my emotions.

Out of the corner of my eye, I noticed the caterpillar slide by and through the crack in the door that led to the attic. I quietly followed him, and I am not sure why. I think that I was still intrigued to see what he would do next and if I could get some answers or reasons why I was in this situation.

Once I climbed the winding stairs and reached the top. I lost sight of my furry little friend. Oh my gosh! My eyes suddenly opened wide as I spotted a very pretty pair of shoes. There they were, the *ribbon bow shoes*, my mom's *ribbon bow shoes*! I was so fond of these white shoes with the yellow, pink, and blue ribbons woven through the shoe's white, mesh material. My mom encouraged us to play dress up and wear the ribbon bow shoes. My sisters and I couldn't wait until it was our turn to wear the ribbon bow shoes. We used to sneak into the attic to play with these special shoes.

In my delight and excitement, I stepped into one of the shoes. The shoe was still a bit big for my foot, but I didn't care. I felt a warm rush tingling throughout my body. It reminded me of how I felt when my mom hugged me. I felt so warm and secure. I picked up the other shoe to put it on my foot. There, all curled up in the shoe, was my friend, the furry caterpillar. He too looked like he was warm and secure. Oh so gently, I laid the shoe on its side to see what the caterpillar would do. He looked up at me and slid out of the shoe as if to let me know it was okay and my turn to wear both shoes.

I didn't waste a minute stepping into the shoe. It was like magic as wonderful memories of my sisters and my mom swirled around in my head. I was so fortunate to have such a close relationship with them. My childhood was special having two sisters. We played dolls, swam at the neighborhood pool, shopped, learned to cook, went ice-skating, and attended sports events, dances, graduations, and so much more.

At the center of these beautiful memories was my mom. She worked to ensure that we valued each other and our family. Dinner time was a sacred event where we came together to share a meal and hear about everyone's day. My mom was kind and giving to us and to others. She was always helping family and friends. She always said, "It doesn't hurt to be kind, and it doesn't cost a cent." I kept thinking about my mom and my sisters.

Suddenly, while standing in the ribbon bow shoes, I felt my ankle begin to wobble. It was a bit of a balancing act trying to stand in shoes that were too big for my feet. Before I knew it, I began to stumble, and the shoes fell off my feet. I looked around, and I was sitting in a chair in my yard. I wasn't in the attic in my childhood home. I didn't feel all warm and tingling.

For another moment, I had to get my bearings. I must have fallen asleep. I was dreaming! I was thinking about my mom and my sisters. How I missed them! I lost my sister Kathy almost nineteen years ago. Yes, she became a cardiac surgical nurse. She knew even as a young child that she wanted to become a nurse. It was very difficult to lose her when she was so young and such a blessing to her patients. About five years ago I lost my sister Jeanne and my mom. My mom passed away that December and Jeanne passed away suddenly in March. Jeanne became a teacher and a principal and shared her love for reading with her students, teachers, and colleagues. I miss our talks and the way we all laughed when we were together. Such good memories of my mom and my sisters still warm my heart!

It is so difficult to lose the people we love. During times of grief, our memories help us to process that loss. Telling stories of your loved ones showcase who they were and provides a wonderful way to honor them. I have changed as a person while working through the struggles of grief. I am strengthened by the pain of loss and softened as I find compassion for others who are also suffering from their losses.

This experience wasn't over for me. The day continued to be warm with the sun shining on my face. I could still smell the nearby lilacs, but I wondered what happened to that caterpillar who led me on my journey of beautiful memories. I stood up and looked around at nature's beauty. My eyes searched for clues or answers to what might have happened. All of a sudden, I saw a cluster of milkweed in the nearby field. There attached to one of the twigs was a chrysalis, and it looked like a butterfly had already emerged.

How I wished I was able to see the butterfly that emerged from that chrysalis. Was it my caterpillar friend who formed that chrysalis? The wind was blowing gently. I could feel it on my hands and my face. I looked down at my hand as I felt something tickle it. There softly perched on my hand was a beautiful butterfly. I know that was my caterpillar, my butterfly! I stood very still to admire his beauty and not to scare him. He stayed perched on my hand for quite a while and then softly fluttered away.

I know that Native Americans thought that butterflies were a symbol of change, transformation, comfort, and hope. I believe my caterpillar, who changed into a beautiful butterfly, was a metaphor, a symbol of hope, transformation, and comfort as I worked through the loss of my mom and my sisters. I hope to see many more butterflies during my lifetime. They are a source of encouragement for me, helping me to understand that healing is possible. I wish you wonderful memories to brighten your days, to help you grow, and to provide comfort when there is pain or loss. I also hope that you find your special butterfly to help you through your journey.

About the Author

Dr. Beth Christoff, a retired elementary art teacher and principal, always possessed a love for writing, drawing, and creating. One item on her bucket list was the desire to write a children's book with an important message. She was fortunate to grow up in a loving family and work with wonderful children and adults throughout her teaching and administrative careers. Her world was shaken by the loss of three very pivotal people in her life. This loss was the inspiration for the creation of this book and a cathartic process for dealing with her loss.